The Sand Tray

First published 2001 by
A & C Black (Publishers) Ltd
37 Soho Square
London WID 3QZ

Text copyright © Citizenship Foundation 2001
Illustrations copyright © Tim Archbold 2001

ISBN 0-7136-5843-6

A CIP catalogue for this book is available from
the British Library.

Published in conjunction with the
Citizenship Foundation.
Sponsored by British Telecom.

Printed in Malta on behalf of
Midas printing (UK) Ltd.

The Sand Tray

by Don Rowe

Illustrated by Tim Archbold

This is Johnny Foster.
He goes to school now, because he is five.

He is in Mrs Smith's class.
Mrs Smith is very nice.

Johnny likes everything at school.

At dinner-time he plays with his friend Tim.

Johnny and Tim have been friends since playgroup.

One day, after dinner, Mrs Smith said
that Johnny and Tim could play in the sand tray
and make up a story.

Johnny and Tim always made up exciting stories
with the cars from the box.
Today they decided to play hospitals.

Johnny's car crashed into a tree.
Tim's ambulance came to the rescue.
It was their best game ever.

Just then, Mrs Smith came up,
holding Kylie's hand.

Kylie was crying because
no one wanted to work with her.

When Mrs Smith asked Kylie
who she wanted to work with,
she said, "Johnny."

Kylie lived next door to Johnny
and they often played together
at home.

"Boys," said Mrs Smith, "Can Kylie play too?
She'd like to join in your story game."

"She can go next, Mrs Smith," said Johnny.
"We're in the middle of the story."

"There are no more good cars, miss," said Tim.
"You can't play without a good car.
Our story is about hospitals and ambulances."

"Well then, Kylie could be a doctor at the hospital,
couldn't she?" said Mrs Smith, smiling.
"There you are, Kylie."

And Mrs Smith walked away to see
who was making a lot of noise
over by the classroom door.

Kylie dried her eyes and stood
watching the game for a minute.
"What can I be?" she asked.

"Nothing," said Tim. Then he had another thought.
"You can be the person that watches us."

"That's not fair," said Kylie.
"Miss said I could play."

Johnny felt bad inside.
At home he played with Kylie a lot.

But not at school.
Tim was his best friend at school.

Johnny didn't look at Kylie, but carried on
building the hospital in the sand.
He stood up to look at it. It was good.

Kylie was starting to cry again.
"Stop it, Kylie," said Johnny.

"You're horrible!" shouted Kylie suddenly, and she knocked Johnny's hospital over with her foot.

"Get off, Kylie!" Johnny shouted, and he pushed
her away so hard that she nearly fell over.
This made her cry even more.

The whole class stopped to
look at what was happening.

"Johnny and Tim!" said Mrs Smith, in a loud voice.
"I asked you to share your
game with Kylie.

Well, if you can't share the sand tray
you'll have to let someone else play there.
You know the rules. Now go and wash your
hands and sit down at your tables."

Johnny and Tim sat down in a bad mood
and started to colour in a picture.
Sometimes Johnny liked colouring, but not today.
He wanted to play in the sand.

"It's not fair!" he said.

Kylie stood by the sand tray and started to play on her own, but it was no fun.

"It's not fair!" she said.

Mrs Smith looked at Johnny, Tim and the whole class.
"Why can't they play nicely just for once?"
she thought.
"My life would be a lot easier."

"It's not fair!"

Something to think about...

Parents or teachers can use these questions as starting points for talking to children about the issues raised in the story.

* Why do you think Johnny and Tim are friends? What kind of friends are they?

* What is a friend? What do friends do for each other?

* Can anyone be your friend? When is someone not your friend?

* Why do you think Johnny and Kylie are friends? What kind of friends are they?

* Do you think Kylie has many friends?

* In the story Johnny has a problem. What is it?

* Do you think it was fair of Miss Smith to ask the boys to let Kylie join in with them? Why do you think that?

* Why did Tim not want to let Kylie play with them? What else could he have done?

* Did Johnny do wrong when he wouldn't let Kylie play with them?

* When is it right to share things and when is it OK not to share?

* Why do you think sharing is hard sometimes?

* The story says that Johnny felt bad inside. What do you think that means? How do you think Tim was feeling?

* Have you ever felt bad inside? What made you feel like that?

* What do you think about the way Johnny and Tim behaved? What words can we use to describe this?

* What do you think about what Kylie did when she broke the game? What words can we use to describe this? Think of some other examples of when people act like this.

* What should happen to Kylie for breaking up the game? Would you be strict with Kylie or not, if you were the teacher? Why?

* Who do you feel most sorry for in the story? Kylie, Johnny, Tim or Miss Smith?

* Which classroom rules do you think Johnny and Tim broke? Why are these rules there?

* Which rules do you find hard to keep? Why is that? Would you change any of these rules if you could?

* Do you think Johnny and Tim were treated fairly or unfairly? Why?

* Why do you think all the people in the story say "It's not fair?" Who do you agree with most? Why is that?